Dear Deer

Dear Deer

A Book of Homophones
GENE BARRETTA

Dear Deer

A Book of Homophones

GENE BARRETTA

SCHOLASTIC INC.
New York   Toronto   London   Auckland
Sydney   Mexico City   New Delhi   Hong Kong

A NOTE TO THE READER

Homophones are words that sound the same but are spelled differently
and have different meanings, such as *moose* (the animal) and *mousse*
(the dessert). *Homonyms* are words that sound the same and are spelled
the same but have different meanings, such as *bowl* (a round dish) and
bowl (the sport).

ISBN-13: 978-0-545-20644-0
ISBN-10: 0-545-20644-8

Copyright © 2007 by Gene Barretta. All rights reserved. Published by Scholastic Inc., 557 Broadway,
New York, NY 10012, by arrangement with Henry Holt and Company, LLC. SCHOLASTIC and associ-
ated logos are trademarks and/or registered trademarks of Scholastic Inc.

12 11 10 9 8 7 6 5 4 3 2   9 10 11 12 13 14/0

Printed in the U.S.A.   08

This edition first printing, September 2009

The artist used watercolor on Arches hot-press paper to create the illustrations for this book.

For my Deerest Leslie (I'm still fawning)

and all my special Ants: Jane, Kathy, Elaine,

Caroline, Dot, Dee, Sandi, Norma, Josie

—Love, Gene

The **MOOSE** loves **MOUSSE**.

He **ATE EIGHT** bowls.

Have **YOU** seen the **EWE**?

She's been in a **DAZE** for **DAYS**.

That's **HIM**, the **HORSE** who is

HOARSE from humming a **HYMN**.

It's quite a **FEAT** when the bat

hangs from his **FEET**.

The monkey will tell you a **TALE** as he hangs from his **TAIL**.

The **DOE KNEADED** the **DOUGH,**

because she **NEEDED** the dough.

The **TOAD** was **TOWED**

to the top of the seesaw,

so he could **SEE** the **SEA**.

The **WHALE** was **ALLOWED**

to **WAIL ALOUD.**

The **BEAR** had to **PAUSE**
to **BARE** his big **PAWS**.

HEY, the elephant **THREW** a pail

THROUGH the big bale of **HAY!**

Have you **READ** about the **RED** fox

who **BLEW BLUE** bubbles?

The giraffe's long neck
lets him CHOOSE
what he CHEWS.

The cows in the **HERD**

were in a good **MOOD**.

I HEARD them as they

MOOED in harmony.

The bee **FLEW** away from the flea with the **FLU**. And the **BEE** can **BE** sure that if he had the flu the **FLEA** would **FLEE**, too.

There is no **NEWS** about the **GNUS**.

They keep to themselves.

AUNT ANT,

You do have some very interesting new neighbors. I have a new neighbor, too! Do you **KNOW** about the **HARE** with **NO HAIR**? She's an expert on skin care.

Love,
Your **DEAR DEER**